ALTO SAXOPHONE

24 Play-along Standards

WITH A LIVE RHYTHM SECTION

Wise Publications
part of The Music Sales Group
London / New York / Paris / Sydney / Copenhagen / Berlin / Madrid / Hong Kong / Tokyo

Published by
Wise Publications
14-15 Berners Street, London W1T 3LJ, UK.

Exclusive Distributors:
Music Sales Limited
Distribution Centre, Newmarket Road, Bury St Edmunds, Suffolk IP33 3YB, UK.
Music Sales Pty Limited
20 Resolution Drive, Caringbah, NSW 2229, Australia.

Order No. AM999240
ISBN 978-1-84938-352-3
This book © Copyright 2010 Wise Publications,
a division of Music Sales Limited.

Edited by Lizzie Moore
Music arranged by Paul Honey
Music processed by Paul Ewers Music Design
Song Background Notes by Michael Heatley
Cover design by Fresh Lemon
Printed in the EU

CD recorded, mixed and mastered by Jonas Persson

Your Guarantee of Quality
As publishers, we strive to produce every book to the highest
commercial standards. This book has been carefully designed
to minimise awkward page turns and to make playing from it
a real pleasure. Particular care has been given to specifying
acid-free, neutral-sized paper made from pulps which have
not been elemental chlorine bleached. This pulp is from farmed
sustainable forests and was produced with special regard for
the environment. Throughout, the printing and binding have
been planned to ensure a sturdy, attractive publication which
should give years of enjoyment. If your copy fails to meet our
high standards, please inform us and we will gladly replace it.

www.musicsales.com

FREE bonus material.

Visit www.hybridpublications.com

Registration is free and easy.

Your registration code is: BU567

Song Background Notes

Birdland - Weather Report

Weather Report, founded by the twin talents of ex-Miles Davis sidemen Joe Zawinul (keyboards) and Wayne Shorter (saxophone), dominated the modern jazz scene in the 1970s. This funky instrumental was penned by Zawinul and named after the New York jazz club on 52nd Street that itself pays homage to saxophonist Charlie 'Bird' Parker. Taken from the album *Heavy Weather*, 'Birdland' became an unlikely US hit single in 1977 and a modern standard that entered the repertoire of bands ranging from Buddy Rich and Maynard Ferguson to The Manhattan Transfer, whose version featured lyrics by Jon Hendricks.

Cantaloupe Island - Herbie Hancock

'Cantaloupe Island', written by keyboardist Herbie Hancock, was first recorded on his 1964 release, Empyrean Isles, one of the most influential jazz albums of the decade. He was still in the Miles Davis band at the time, and the album featured the Davis rhythm section of Hancock, Ron Carter and Tony Williams with the addition of Freddie Hubbard on cornet. It was one of the first examples of a modal jazz composition set to a funky beat, and its ahead-of-time credentials were confirmed when the jazz/rap group US3 sampled it a quarter of a century later on the song 'Cantaloop'.

Chan Chan - Compay Segundo

Cuba's Compay Segundo was already approaching his nineties when fame, in the shape of Ry Cooder, came calling. Born Máximo Francisco Repilado Muñoz in 1907, he began his career singing with bands in the 1920s. He gained fame in the 1940s as one half of the Los Compadres duo, then formed his own band, Los Muchachos. He was also an accomplished guitarist and latterly played a unique seven-stringed tres (double-stringed guitar) which he designed himself. Captured by film-maker Wim Wenders in his *Buena Vista Social Club* movie of 1999, Segundo rode the wave of international interest in traditional Cuban music, and 'Chan Chan' is typical of the island's 'golden age' which extended from the 1930s to 1950s.

Crazy Rhythm - Chet Baker

Although Oklahoma-born trumpeter Chet Baker died in 1988, his music found a fresh audience as a new millennium began thanks to extensive use of his music in the Oscar-nominated movie *The Talented Mr Ripley*. The number 'Crazy Rhythm' first surfaced in 1928 when it was written by Irving Caesar, Joseph Meyer and Roger Wolfe Kahn for the Broadway musical *Here's Howe*. The swinging 32-bar showtune, first recorded by Roger Wolfe Kahn's Orchestra, has since become a jazz standard thanks to Baker and others.

The Girl From Ipanema (Garota de Ipanema) - Antonio Carlos Jobim

'The Girl From Ipanema' brought Brazilian music to a worldwide audience in the 1960s thanks to composer/performers Antonio Carlos Jobim and João Gilberto from Brazil, allied to the talents of US jazzman Stan Getz. Gilberto, from Bahia in northern Brazil, was first to record 'Ipanema', singing in Portuguese, but it was when sung in English that it reached No. 5 in the American charts in 1964, with Gilberto's wife Astrud on vocals, joined by Getz and Jobim. While the bossa-nova craze has loosened its hold on both the jazz and popular music worlds, radio stations worldwide still resurrect this attractively rhythmic item on a regular basis.

Hi-Heel Sneakers - Tommy Tucker

Ohio-born singer-keyboardist Robert Higginbotham changed his name to Tommy Tucker and found fame in 1964 with this self-penned R&B classic that crossed over to the US pop Top 20 on Chess Records' subsidiary Checker label. The version issued was the original demo recording. Since then everybody from Elvis through The Beatles to Tom Jones has covered his first and greatest three minutes. When his follow-up, the similar 'Long Tall Shorty', failed to scale the charts, Tucker retired from music to become an estate agent!

I Get The Sweetest Feeling - Jackie Wilson

Three times a hit in Britain, this feel-good track from soul legend Jackie Wilson was a US hit in the late 1960s. It started life as a Motown song co-written by Van McCoy (of 'The Hustle' fame) and Alicia Evelyn, but quickly became Wilson's own with help from orchestrator Willie Henderson. After the chart-topping success of the Claymation video-led re-release of 'Reet Petite' in 1986, two years after Wilson's death, this track was also re-released and peaked at No. 3 in the UK Chart. The song was used in the movie *High Fidelity*, and cover versions have been recorded by Will Young and Atomic Kitten Liz McClarnon.

Knock On Wood - Eddie Floyd

The similarity between Eddie Floyd's biggest hit 'Knock On Wood' and Wilson Pickett's 'In The Midnight Hour' may have stemmed from co-writer Steve Cropper, who assisted both singers, and stopped the former being released until 1966, the year after 'In The Midnight Hour' made it into the charts. 'Knock On Wood' was written on a stormy night, hence the lyrical reference to thunder and lightning, and may well have been intended for Otis Redding, whose belated duet version of the song with Carla Thomas emerged in 1967. The song was also covered successfully by disco diva Amii Stewart (UK No. 6, 1979) and David Bowie (UK No. 10, 1974).

Lean On Me - Bill Withers

When Bill Withers bought a new electric piano in the early 1970s to celebrate changing career from being an aircraft mechanic to a recording artist, 'Lean On Me' was the very first thing he wrote. He admitted he had no idea what the notes were: 'I found these spaces on the keys and liked the sound. I was going up and down and it sounded like some of those hymns I grew up with. So I kept doing it 'cause I liked it'. The title and lyrics were inspired by a poor upbringing in West Virginia where nobody had very much and neighbours would rally round to help those in need. The result was a modern classic.

Mas Que Nada - Jorge Ben / Sérgio Mendes

The Portuguese-lyric signature song of Sergio Mendes & Brasil 66, Jorge Ben's 'Mas Que Nada' gained a new lease of life when it appeared on the *Austin Powers: International Man of Mystery* soundtrack. The title, in Brazilian-Portuguese slang, means 'Come On' or 'No Way'. In 2006 Mendes re-recorded the song with The Black Eyed Peas and additional vocals by wife Gracinha Leporace, including it on his album *Timeless*. In Brazil the song is also well known for being the theme song for television channel Globos Estrelas. The samba has a rolling rhythm that gets your body moving, and 'Mas Que Nada' never fails to work its magic.

Need Your Love So Bad - Fleetwood Mac

Fleetwood Mac took a song by jailed bluesman Little Willie John and produced not only the definitive version, but a 1968 UK hit available on the *Pious Bird Of Good Omen* album. Band founder, singer and guitarist Peter Green had first heard the original while working with John Mayall's Bluesbreakers; Mayall played him B. B. King's version, inspiring Green to employ Mickey Baker of Mickey and Sylvia 'Love Is Strange' fame to orchestrate the now-customary ear-catching backing strings.

Nobody Knows The Trouble I've Seen - Louis Armstrong

This spiritual was definitively interpreted by Louis Armstrong, though folk/blues singer Leadbelly, aka Huddie Ledbetter, also recorded a memorable version for the Library of Congress in the early 1940s. Pastor's son Sam Cooke's later take is perhaps one of the most poignant as he led a short but troubled life before dying violently in 1964 at the age of just 33. He'd suffered mental turmoil after rejecting a gospel career with the Soul Stirrers for the rewards of pop stardom, only to die in a motel shooting resulting from his tangled private life.

Please Send Me Someone To Love - Percy Mayfield

This R&B chart-topping blues ballad was written and recorded by Percy Mayfield for Specialty Records in 1950. It was a prayer-like lyric that not only covered affairs of the heart but also, rarely for the time, included a demand for racial tolerance long before (the unrelated) Curtis Mayfield and Marvin Gaye made such things popular. Jeff Buckley, Slade and B. B. King are among its coverers. Mayfield, who is best known for writing Ray Charles' No. 1 'Hit The Road, Jack', was facially disfigured in a car crash two years after this recording.

Satin Doll - Duke Ellington / Billy Strayhorn

Duke Ellington's golden era from the late-'20s to the mid-'40s in which he made his name as both a writer and bandleader, was given a further dimension with the recruitment of pianist/arranger Billy Strayhorn in 1939. The lyrics to 'Satin Doll' were written by Johnny Mercer after the song was already a hit in its instrumental form, Ellington having used it as the closing number at most of his concerts, and it has since been recorded by such illustrious artists as Ella Fitzgerald and Frank Sinatra.

So What - Miles Davis

Whenever there was a stylistic innovation in post-war jazz, the name of Miles Davis was rarely far away. 'So What' was the opening track of his groundbreaking *Kind Of Blue* album, released in 1959 and astonishingly recorded in just nine hours in two sessions at Columbia's 30th Street New York studio. Davis' band had never played the numbers before, the trumpeter believing this would inspire their best performances, and like all but one track, 'So What' was a first take—spontaneity at its brilliant best. It's been said that arranger Gil Evans wrote the introduction, described by one critic as 'perhaps the most beautiful 30 seconds or so in all of jazz'.

(Something Inside) So Strong - Labi Siffre

When, in the 1980s, British singer-songwriter Labi Siffre saw a television report on killings in Africa and saw one of the perpetrators smiling, he channelled his outrage and disgust into a potent and deeply spiritual song. When two major artists turned it down for being 'too controversial' and 'one-sided', he left self-imposed retirement, having previously decided to concentrate on writing rather than performing, to record it himself and was rewarded by a UK Top 10 hit.

Son Of A Preacher Man - Dusty Springfield

The success of the album *Dusty In Memphis*, of which this was the killer cut, underlined the fact that soul comes from within and is not determined by skin colour. The former Mary O'Brien had travelled to the Stax studios in 1968 and was offered the song only after Aretha Franklin turned it down. By the time Lady Soul reconsidered, Dusty's version had become definitive. A transatlantic Top 10 entry in early 1969, this would be Dusty Springfield's last hit for 20 years. The song has been covered by innumerable female singers but it was the original that featured in the 1994 film *Pulp Fiction*.

Sway (¿Quién Será?) - Pablo Beltrán Ruiz

'¿Quién Será?', a song in the infectious mambo style released in 1953 by Mexican composer and bandleader Pablo Beltrán Ruiz, reached a worldwide audience the following year when Dean Martin's cover reached No. 15 in the USA and No. 6 in the UK. The added ingredient was English lyrics by Norman Gimbel and the Anglicised title 'Sway', but the instrumental original is hot stuff in its own right! To prove its international credentials, '¿Quién Será?', literally 'Who Will It Be?', has been recorded in languages as diverse as Turkish and, by Björk, in Icelandic. The mambo resulted from a fusion of swing and Cuban music and led to the cha-cha-chá. It is as challenging to play as to dance, but swaying can pay dividends!

'Tain't What You Do (It's The Way That Cha Do It) - Sy Oliver / Jimmie Lunceford

The combination of bandleader Jimmie Lunceford and arranger Sy Oliver resulted in some memorable music created in just a few late-'30s years. "Tain't What You Do...' was just one of the swing classics they wrote together, exhibiting Oliver's trademarks of, "Two-beat rhythm, stop-time breaks, intricate saxophone choruses and ear-splitting brass explosions". Oliver defected to Tommy Dorsey in 1939, but "Tain't What You Do...' lived on in the hands of Ella Fitzgerald, the Fun Boy Three and many others.

Take Five - Dave Brubeck

One of the most popular jazz musicians of the last century, keyboardist and bandleader Dave Brubeck arguably did more to promote modern jazz than any other player. His alto saxophonist Paul Desmond wrote 'Take Five', the first and biggest of a series of pop hits for Brubeck's Quartet that brought the concept of modern jazz to a whole new generation in 1960–61. Brubeck experimented with time signatures through much of his career (Take Five is in 5/4 time), while Desmond, who died in 1977, left all future royalties from the jazz classic he penned to the American Red Cross.

The Thrill Is Gone - B. B. King

B. B. King's first success outside the blues market was his 1969 recording of 'The Thrill Is Gone'. He had heard blues pianist/composer Roy Hawkins perform 'and I thought it was a good idea so I re-wrote the tune. The lines you hear are the ones that I wrote. I carried it around with me for eight years but we'd never hit it like I wanted it. But that night everything seemed to be just right.' The song also benefited from a string arrangement from Bert DeCoteaux. King's version became a hit on both pop and R&B charts while he promoted it as opening act on The Rolling Stones' American tour.

Try A Little Tenderness - Otis Redding

Written by Irving King (a pseudonym used by the song-writing duo James Campbell and Reginald Connelly) and Harry M. Woods, this song dates back to 1933 and crooner Bing Crosby. Aretha Franklin was the first to record it soul-style in 1962, but all subsequent performances by the likes of Rod Stewart and Tina Turner have referenced Otis Redding's definitive 1966 version which progresses from balladic beginning to stomping climax in three and a half minutes. The only version Otis knew, by idol and mentor, Sam Cooke, featured just two verses as it was part of a live medley, so he performed it that way too. The song was brought to a new generation on the big screen in 1991 by The Commitments.

Tuxedo Junction - Erskine Hawkins / Glenn Miller

Though his aeroplane went down in mysterious circumstances in 1944, Glenn Miller's musical legacy continues to fly high today. His trademark sound was the combination of clarinet and four saxes plus the repeated riff that fades away before reappearing. Erskine Hawkins, who wrote 'Tuxedo Junction' was a prominent African-American trumpeter, bandleader and Miller contemporary during the big-band era. He named the number after an area of Birmingham, Alabama.

Wade In The Water - The Staple Singers

Some musicologists believe 'Wade In The Water' can be traced back to slavery days. Such songs were passed on by word of mouth, and the title may advise runaway slaves on how to avoid being tracked by hounds. Taken literally, the words reflect the Israelites' escape from Egypt, while the reference to the safe haven of 'Jordan' could also be Canada, where slavery did not exist. Whatever the truth, 'Wade In The Water' was an instrumental pop hit in 1966 for the Ramsey Lewis Trio, inspiring similar recordings by Herb Alpert and Billy Preston, as well as numerous vocal renditions.

Birdland

Words by Jon Hendricks
Music by Josef Zawinul

Demo track: CD1 Track 01
Backing track: CD2 Track 01

Crazy Rhythm

Words by Irving Caesar
Music by Joseph Meyer & Roger Wolfe Kahn

Demo track: CD1 Track 02
Backing track: CD2 Track 02

cresc.

Cantaloupe Island

Music by Herbie Hancock

Demo track: CD1 Track 03
Backing track: CD2 Track 03

Moderately ♩ = 114

Chan Chan

Words & Music by Francisco Repilado

Demo track: CD1 Track 04
Backing track: CD2 Track 04

The Girl From Ipanema

Original Words by Vinicius De Moraes
English Words by Norman Gimbel
Music by Antonio Carlos Jobim

Demo track: CD1 Track 05
Backing track: CD2 Track 05

Hi-Heel Sneakers

Words & Music by Robert Higgenbotham

Demo track: CD1 Track 06
Backing track: CD2 Track 06

I Get The Sweetest Feeling

Words & Music by Van McCoy & Alicia Evelyn

Demo track: CD1 Track 07
Backing track: CD2 Track 07

Knock On Wood

Words & Music by Steve Cropper & Eddie Floyd

Demo track: CD1 Track 08
Backing track: CD2 Track 08

Lean On Me

Words & Music by Bill Withers

Demo track: CD1 Track 09
Backing track: CD2 Track 09

Mas Que Nada

Words & Music by Jorge Ben

Demo track: CD1 Track 10
Backing track: CD2 Track 10

Bright Samba feel

Need Your Love So Bad

Words & Music by Mertis John Jr.

Demo track: CD1 Track 11
Backing track: CD2 Track 11

Steadily

Please Send Me Someone To Love

Demo track: CD1 Track 12
Backing track: CD2 Track 12

Words & Music by Percy Mayfield

33

Satin Doll

Words by Johnny Mercer
Music by Duke Ellington & Billy Strayhorn

Demo track: CD1 Track 13
Backing track: CD2 Track 13

Moderate swing

(Something Inside) So Strong

Words & Music by Labi Siffre

Demo track: CD1 Track 14
Backing track: CD2 Track 14

Son Of A Preacher Man

Words & Music by John Hurley & Ronnie Wilkins

Demo track: CD1 Track 15
Backing track: CD2 Track 15

poco rall.

So What

Music by Miles Davis

Demo track: CD1 Track 16
Backing track: CD2 Track 16

Moderate swing feel ♩ = 142

Sway (¿Quién Será?)

Words & Music by Pablo Beltran Ruiz

Demo track: CD1 Track 17
Backing track: CD2 Track 17

Moderate Cha-Cha-Chá

'Tain't What You Do
(It's The Way That Cha Do It)

Demo track: CD1 Track 18
Backing track: CD2 Track 18

Words & Music by Sy Oliver & James Young

Easy swing feel

Take Five

Music by Paul Desmond

Demo track: CD1 Track 19
Backing track: CD2 Track 19

The Thrill Is Gone

Words & Music by Roy Hawkins & Rick Darnell

Demo track: CD1 Track 20
Backing track: CD2 Track 20

Moderately ♩ = 90

Try A Little Tenderness

Words & Music by Harry Woods, Jimmy Campbell & Reg Connelly

Demo track: CD1 Track 21
Backing track: CD2 Track 21

Tuxedo Junction

**Words & Music by Buddy Feyne, Erskine Hawkins,
William Johnson & Julian Dash**

Demo track: CD1 Track 22
Backing track: CD2 Track 22

Wade In The Water

Traditional

Demo track: CD1 Track 23
Backing track: CD2 Track 23

Optional 16 bar ad lib. solo

Nobody Knows The Trouble I've Seen

Demo track: CD1 Track 24
Backing track: CD2 Track 24

Traditional

Optional 16 bar ad lib. solo

456789

CD TRACK LISTING

CD 1
DEMONSTRATION TRACKS

1 Birdland (Hendricks/Zawinul)
Campbell Connelly & Company Limited/Notting Hill Music (UK) Limited.

2 Crazy Rhythm (Caesar/Meyer/Kahn)
Redwood Music Limited/Warner/Chappell North America Limited.

3 Cantaloupe Island (Hancock)
Sony/ATV Music Publishing (UK) Limited.

4 Chan Chan (Repilado)
Universal Music Publishing MGB Limited.

5 The Girl From Ipanema
(Garota de Ipanema) (Jobim/De Moraes/Gimbel)
SACEM/Universal Music Publishing Limited/Windswept Music (London) Limited.

6 Hi-Heel Sneakers (Higgenbotham)
Jewel Music Publishing Company Limited.

7 I Get The Sweetest Feeling (McCoy/Evelyn)
T M Music Limited.

8 Knock On Wood (Cropper/Floyd)
Universal Music Publishing Limited/Warner/Chappell Music Limited.

9 Lean On Me (Withers)
Universal/MCA Music Limited.

10 Mas Que Nada (Ben)
Latin-American Music Publishing Company Limited.

11 Need Your Love So Bad (John)
Lark Music Limited.

12 Please Send Me Someone To Love (Mayfield)
Sony/ATV Music Publishing (UK) Limited.

13 Satin Doll (Mercer/Ellington/Strayhorn)
Campbell Connelly & Company Limited.

14 (Something Inside) So Strong (Siffre)
Universal Music Publishing Limited.

15 Son Of A Preacher Man (Hurley/Wilkins)
Sony/ATV Music Publishing (UK) Limited.

16 So What (Davis)
Universal/MCA Music Limited.

17 Sway (¿Quién Será?) (Ruiz)
Latin-American Music Publishing Company Limited.

18 'Tain't What You Do
(It's The Way That Cha Do It) (Oliver/Young)
Universal/MCA Music Limited.

19 Take Five (Desmond)
The Valentine Music Group Limited.

20 The Thrill Is Gone (Hawkins/Darnell)
Universal Music Publishing MGB Limited.

21 Try A Little Tenderness (Woods/Campbell/Connelly)
Campbell Connelly & Company Limited.

22 Tuxedo Junction (Feyne/Hawkins/Johnson/Dash)
Lafleur Music Limited.

23 Wade In The Water (Trad)
Dorsey Brothers Music Limited.

24 Nobody Knows The Trouble I've Seen (Trad)
Dorsey Brothers Music Limited.

CD 2
BACKING TRACKS

1 Birdland

2 Crazy Rhythm

3 Cantaloupe Island

4 Chan Chan

5 The Girl From Ipanema (Garota de Ipanema)

6 Hi-Heel Sneakers

7 I Get The Sweetest Feeling

8 Knock On Wood

9 Lean On Me

10 Mas Que Nada

11 Need Your Love So Bad

12 Please Send Me Someone To Love

13 Satin Doll

14 (Something Inside) So Strong

15 Son Of A Preacher Man

16 So What

17 Sway (¿Quién Será?)

18 'Tain't What You Do
(It's The Way That Cha Do It)

19 Take Five

20 The Thrill Is Gone

21 Try A Little Tenderness

22 Tuxedo Junction

23 Wade In The Water

24 Nobody Knows The Trouble I've Seen

To remove your CD from the plastic sleeve, lift the small lip to break the perforations. Replace the disc after use for convenient storage.